General Conference
Activity Book
For Kids 4-12

My Name:

_____

11 Different Activities filling 90+ pages
Activities range from simple to more
challenging
Providing hours of entertainment and
learning while watching
General Conference or just for FUN!!

Table of Contents

I Spy

I SPY...in the Springtime

I SPY...in my Home

Spot the Difference

Spot the 5 Differences - #1

Spot the 5 Differences - #2

Word Searches

I Love to See the Temple

Y	S	T	C	K	U	C	A
I	L	B	E	A	U	T	Y
N	Q	O	G	M	N	J	U
S	T	J	V	O	P	P	K
I	P	G	D	E	I	L	A
D	L	I	S	T	E	N	E
E	B	V	P	R	A	Y	G
R	S	P	I	R	I	T	G

BEAUTY   GOING
INSIDE   LISTEN
LOVE   PRAY
SPIRIT   TEMPLE

I Am a Child of God

P	A	R	E	N	T	S	Y
L	O	F	W	T	H	C	O
R	V	T	N	S	O	H	L
Q	Z	E	D	G	M	I	E
M	S	E	G	O	E	L	A
V	E	D	B	D	T	D	R
N	X	V	A	R	V	M	N
D	W	A	L	K	A	A	U

CHILD
HOME
NEEDS
SENT

GOD
LEARN
PARENTS
WALK

Follow the Prophet

A	B	R	A	H	A	M	I
P	G	M	A	D	A	M	W
W	R	N	O	E	Q	O	Q
H	O	O	B	S	L	P	J
J	Q	A	P	L	E	P	X
B	R	H	O	H	L	S	B
V	G	F	O	M	E	A	B
S	A	M	U	E	L	T	I

ABRAHAM
FOLLOW
MOSES
PROPHET

ADAM
JONAH
NOAH
SAMUEL

Families Can Be Together Forever

```
S   F   O   R   E   V   E   R

F   A   M   I   L   Y   F   S

F   M   A   R   R   Y   P   H

W   E   A   R   T   H   L   O

K   V   R   J   N   U   A   W

K   O   B   L   X   Q   N   N

I   Z   H   E   A   V   E   N

M   F   A   T   H   E   R   S
```

EARTH	FAMILY
FATHERS	FOREVER
HEAVEN	MARRY
PLAN	SHOWN

13

I Know My Father Lives

D	H	B	S	P	I	R	I	T	R
I	S	D	T	W	M	Z	H	X	O
H	K	S	S	E	N	T	B	V	W
T	C	P	H	U	I	J	W	X	H
F	L	L	W	A	I	H	W	L	I
A	E	L	F	K	L	O	V	E	S
T	P	A	I	Q	N	Y	Z	S	P
H	Z	L	R	V	P	O	X	J	E
E	X	Y	A	T	E	H	W	Q	R
R	K	N	Q	N	H	S	R	U	S

EARTH	FAITH
FATHER	KNOW
LIVES	LOVES
PLAN	SENT
SPIRIT	WHISPERS

I Lived in Heaven

```
L   E   G   E   K   A   X   P   V   C
V   Y   X   K   H   B   J   E   B   L
W   C   N   U   H   O   D   O   A   W
E   P   X   L   O   V   F   P   Q   A
T   J   L   L   O   E   M   L   R   I
E   O   K   A   I   V   G   E   E   T
R   N   Y   D   N   V   E   W   T   I
N   F   Y   Y   J   I   E   D   U   N
A   Q   M   T   R   U   E   D   R   G
L   R   H   E   A   V   E   N   N   D
```

ABOVE	ETERNAL
HEAVEN	LIVED
LOVED	PEOPLE
PLAN	RETURN
TRUE	WAITING

I Hope They Call Me On a Mission

P	R	E	A	C	H	C	Y	E	R
I	Z	S	U	F	C	X	Q	G	Z
D	H	O	P	E	O	S	H	O	K
W	O	R	K	D	C	O	U	S	M
X	E	J	G	L	Y	A	T	P	I
I	T	S	P	R	U	W	L	E	S
U	D	E	H	J	O	F	L	L	S
U	X	B	A	A	K	W	Z	P	I
E	K	T	M	C	R	E	N	D	O
B	T	G	U	N	H	E	H	F	N

CALL
GOSPEL
HOPE
PREACH
TEACH

FOOT
GROWN
MISSION
SHARE
WORK

Book of Mormon Stories

U	T	E	A	C	H	E	R	M	Z
A	Y	Y	Y	S	M	D	J	W	B
N	D	B	Z	D	O	H	L	M	U
C	X	L	N	M	R	I	I	S	S
I	A	A	Y	A	M	S	B	E	T
E	L	O	Z	F	O	T	E	E	O
N	S	P	T	R	N	O	R	K	R
T	E	W	U	E	P	R	T	I	I
Y	Q	C	D	E	Q	Y	Y	N	E
B	R	O	T	H	E	R	S	G	S

MORMON   ANCIENT
BROTHERS   FREE
HISTORY   LAND
LIBERTY   SEEKING
STORIES   TEACHER

CHALLENGE - Old Testament Prophets

```
X E W A M A L A C H I R W H Q
U V V U C U A E H R C T A E E
I T M J L P M M N F Q I J H X
W R W M I C A H O O A J S A U
T J J T S G P T S S C G Q G A
H E O N F T Y E I N U H W G H
A R S A B X S J O N A H C A H
B E H H Z O M E Z A R G I I V
A M U U M A U J Z C D D H H I
K I A M H I D O G E A A T N L
K A Q A A M S E X B K K M T Y
U H R L D V W L O W F I A D V
K B N O A H B H O S E A E Y O
A H Z E C H A R I A H S R L M
Z E P H A N I A H S A M U E L
```

ABRAHAM	ADAM
AMOS	ENOCH
EZEKIEL	HABAKKUK
HAGGAI	HOSEA
ISAIAH	JEREMIAH
JOEL	JONAH
JOSHUA	MALACHI
MICAH	MOSES
NAHUM	NOAH
OBADIAH	SAMUEL
ZECHARIAH	ZEPHANIAH

CHALLENGE - First Presidency & 12 Apostles

```
D K A U Q O F S V Q S B S E R D D X Y Z
T D F S Y K L X D U E K T A N N C W Y N
O I L I C L L Y T K A J N A U A N J B B
D E N S W L F K V O F D B L G E A E K M
D T K R U O W Y H A E S N N L J M F B R
C E N S F G M N S B A E I C J D E F Y U
H R Q R N D I I A R R R N X S K Q R Q S
R F R I P L D D A G Y G H K T N V E Q S
I U H T L A I D E E I P T X L R S Y U E
S C E A E V L L B U W K F W F N O R E L
T H D V A A A Y T N U K G Y V Z E H N L
O T K D N D R S E U N L H O O L F O T B
F D O O S N C S E I N J H G E Q K L I A
F O R W E C T T J I S O X N X U B L N L
E R L H G E R R I T W G O N G I D A L L
R F V B N F Z J Y Z B R M R G W Z N C A
S E F Q N E I L L A N D E R S E N D O R
O J R U S S E L L M N E L S O N S A O D
N F R G A R Y E S T E V E N S O N I K V
B F Y Y E U L I S S E S S O A R E S M S
```

D TODD CHRISTOFFERSON
DALE G RENLUND
DAVID A BEDNAR
GARY E STEVENSON
HENRY B EYRING
M RUSSELL BALLARD
QUENTIN L COOK
RUSSELL M NELSON

DALLIN H OAKS
DIETER F UCHTDORF
GERRIT W GONG
JEFFREY R HOLLAND
NEIL L ANDERSEN
RONALD A RASBAND
ULISSES SOARES

Sudoku

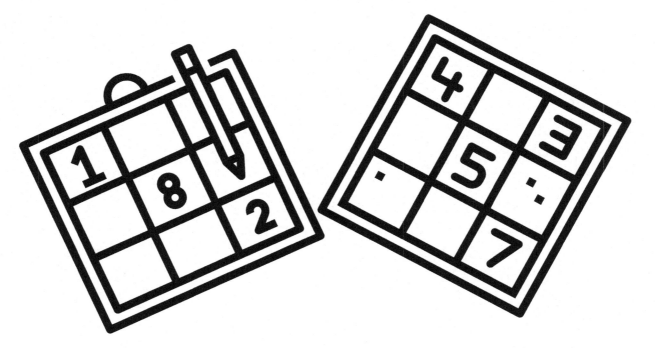

Puzzle #1

6x6 Sudoku

		4			1
1	5	6		2	
		5	1		3
	1		2		6
			4	1	
5		1			2

Puzzle #2

6x6 Sudoku

	6	4		1	
	2			6	
		6		5	
4			6	2	1
6	3	1	2	4	5
5				3	6

Puzzle #3

6x6 Sudoku

	2		4	6	5
4	5	6	3		1
					6
6	4	5	2		3
		4		3	
2	3	1	6	5	

Puzzle #4

6x6 Sudoku

1	5	3		2	4
4					
6	4	1			
5		2	4	1	6
		5	3	4	1
	1	4	5		2

Puzzle #1

9x9 Sudoku

8	1	5	9			2	6	
9		4			3	1		
	6	3	8	2		9	5	
3	7	2	4		5		1	
6								
				1	7	5		
5	8		3				7	
		6	7	8		4		
						3	9	

Puzzle #2

9x9 Sudoku

						2		
5		2		3	8	9		
1			5	2	9	3		6
		5	1			8	4	2
		1	3	4	5	7	6	
	6	7					5	3
			9		3			
9	4	8			6			1
2	5		4		1			

Puzzle #3

9x9 Sudoku

9			3	2	4	7	5	
	3			6				4
		5	1			2		3
6			9	1	7	5		
				8			7	
	2	3	4					
5	6		8	4	2			9
		8		3		6		
3			6				2	

Puzzle #4

9x9 Sudoku

				4		2		
		4	9		2		8	
					5			3
		9	8		4	3		1
2	1	8					6	7
				1	7	9	5	
8		3		2		7		6
7			6		8			
4				5	9	8	3	2

cesdra

bmeemr

anuoov

atrwe

Word Scrambles

ylho hgsto

gghaai

hona

emoss

2022 12 APOSTLES

M URSESLL ALABDRL

_ _ _ _ _ _ _ _ _ _ _ _ _ _

TEDEIR F CUTOFHDR

_ _ _ _ _ _ _ _ _ _ _ _ _

IREGTR W OGGN

_ _ _ _ _ _ _ _ _ _ _ _

ERFYEFJ R LHNAODL

_ _ _ _ _ _ _ _ _ _ _ _ _

AEDL G LDNRUNE

_ _ _ _ _ _ _ _ _ _ _ _ _

IENL L ENANERSD

_ _ _ _ _ _ _ _ _ _ _ _

TNNQUIE L KCOO

_ _ _ _ _ _ _ _ _ _ _ _ _

SLSISUE EASSRO

_ _ _ _ _ _ _ _ _ _ _ _ _

OARLDN A ASNDARB

_ _ _ _ _ _ _ _ _ _ _ _ _

D DOTD OSTRIHCFOEFNRS

_ _ _ _ _ _ _ _ _ _ _ _ _ _

AVDID A DAENBR

_ _ _ _ _ _ _ _ _ _ _ _ _

YAGR E TESSVNEON

_ _ _ _ _ _ _ _ _ _ _ _ _

BAPTISM RELATED WORDS

CESDRA

_ _ _ _ _ _

VNANTECO

_ _ _ _ _ _ _ _

BMEEMR

_ _ _ _ _ _

EBIDAPZT

_ _ _ _ _ _ _ _

ENIMOSIMR

_ _ _ _ _ _ _ _ _

YLHO HGSTO

_ _ _ _ _ _ _ _ _ _

SJUSE SHCTRI

_ _ _ _ _ _ _ _ _ _ _ _

DMNSTONEACMM

_ _ _ _ _ _ _ _ _ _ _

ETIHW TCOSHLE

_ _ _ _ _ _ _ _ _ _ _ _ _

TIOPDSHERO

_ _ _ _ _ _ _ _ _ _

ATRWE

_ _ _ _ _

MTOOCIANNFIR

_ _ _ _ _ _ _ _ _ _ _ _

OLD TESTAMENT PROPHETS #1

AKBKHKUA   _ _ _ _ _ _ _

HEPZANIHA   _ _ _ _ _ _ _ _

GGHAAI   _ _ _ _ _ _

EIAARHZCH   _ _ _ _ _ _ _ _ _

AALMCHI   _ _ _ _ _ _ _

SAAHII   _ _ _ _ _ _

DAMA   _ _ _ _

CONEH   _ _ _ _ _

RBAAHAM   _ _ _ _ _ _ _

EMOSS   _ _ _ _ _

HONA   _ _ _ _

OLD TESTAMENT PROPHETS #2

SAUOHJ   _ _ _ _ _ _

USLEAM   _ _ _ _ _ _

HIAEJRME   _ _ _ _ _ _ _ _

ZEKLIEE   _ _ _ _ _ _ _

SHAEO   _ _ _ _ _

LEJO   _ _ _ _

MSOA   _ _ _ _

AHOBDAI   _ _ _ _ _ _ _

HNAJO   _ _ _ _ _

ACMIH   _ _ _ _ _

HNMAU   _ _ _ _ _

PLACES IN CHURCH HISTORY

ALPAMRY   _ _ _ _ _ _

LHLI MUCAORH   _ _ _ _ _ _ _ _ _ _ _

TKRIANDL   _ _ _ _ _ _ _ _

ANUOOV   _ _ _ _ _ _

RFA EWTS   _ _ _ _ _ _ _

ANCJKOS UYOTCN   _ _ _ _ _ _ _ _ _ _ _ _

LSTA KLEA YCIT   _ _ _ _ _ _ _ _ _ _ _ _

OAHRYMN   _ _ _ _ _ _ _

CSDREA OVREG   _ _ _ _ _ _ _ _ _ _ _

NETIRW RARUSTEQ   _ _ _ _ _ _ _ _ _ _ _ _ _

AGACTHRE   _ _ _ _ _ _ _ _

ITRLBEY IJAL   _ _ _ _ _ _ _ _ _ _ _

ORIGINAL 12 APOSTLES

EERPT   _ _ _ _ _

DENWAR   _ _ _ _ _ _

SAMJE   _ _ _ _ _

NHOJ   _ _ _ _

HTEDDUSA   _ _ _ _ _ _ _ _

IHIPLP   _ _ _ _ _ _

MTERHOWBA   _ _ _ _ _ _ _ _ _

HMTSAO   _ _ _ _ _ _

ISMON   _ _ _ _ _

AJDSU ORIATISC   _ _ _ _ _ _ _ _ _ _ _ _ _

EAJSM   _ _ _ _ _

EMTTHAW   _ _ _ _ _ _ _

BOOK OF MORMON PROPHETS #1

HINPE   _ _ _ _ _

BOCJA   _ _ _ _ _

ONSE   _ _ _ _

NIBIADA   _ _ _ _ _ _ _

IGKN EAIBNNMJ   _ _ _ _ _ _ _ _ _ _ _ _

AOMISH   _ _ _ _ _ _

MLAA   _ _ _ _

LMAA ETH GRNOEYU   _ _ _ _ _ _ _ _ _ _ _ _ _ _

NRMIOO   _ _ _ _ _ _

36 OMROMN   _ _ _ _ _ _

BOOK OF MORMON PROPHETS #2

ERJDA

_ _ _ _ _

OEHTRBR FO AJDRE

_ _ _ _ _ _ _ _ _ _ _ _ _ _

HETER

_ _ _ _ _

AHNEMAL

_ _ _ _ _ _ _

OMMAN

_ _ _ _ _

RAAON

_ _ _ _ _

MRIEHN

_ _ _ _ _ _

NATIAPC OIOMRN

_ _ _ _ _ _ _ _ _ _ _ _ _

IELH

_ _ _ _

IHBAS

_ _ _ _ _

ULSEAM

_ _ _ _ _ _

BOOK OF MORMON 12 APOSTLES

IPEHN   _ _ _ _ _

ITTMHYO   _ _ _ _ _ _ _

NOASJ   _ _ _ _ _

ITMNAHO   _ _ _ _ _ _ _

AAOIMHHNTH   _ _ _ _ _ _ _ _ _ _

MUKNE   _ _ _ _ _

MUKHEOINN   _ _ _ _ _ _ _ _ _

IHEEJARM   _ _ _ _ _ _ _ _

OMHSNEN   _ _ _ _ _ _ _

OANSJ   _ _ _ _ _

EHEAKIDZ   _ _ _ _ _ _ _ _

HAIIAS   _ _ _ _ _ _

7 DISPENSATION LEADERS

DAMA   _ _ _ _

HENCO   _ _ _ _ _

ONAH   _ _ _ _

RBAMHAA   _ _ _ _ _ _ _

OSMES   _ _ _ _ _

IHRTCS   _ _ _ _ _ _

SOEJHP IHTMS   _ _ _ _ _ _ _ _ _ _ _ _

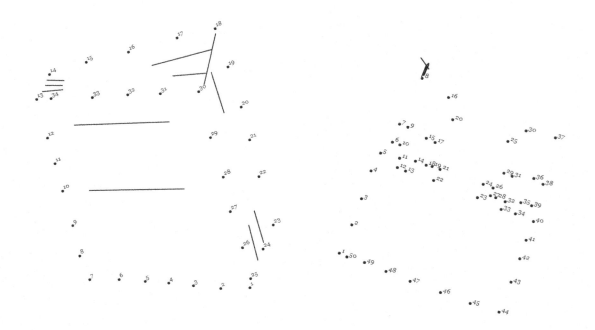

Dot-to-Dot

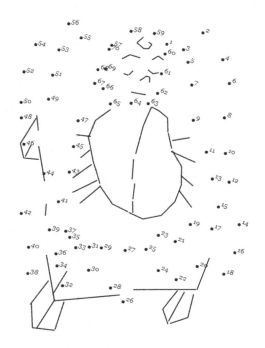

What is the name of this book?

B_o_ o_ M_r_o_

#2

What does CTR stand for?

C_o_s_ t_e R_g_t

42

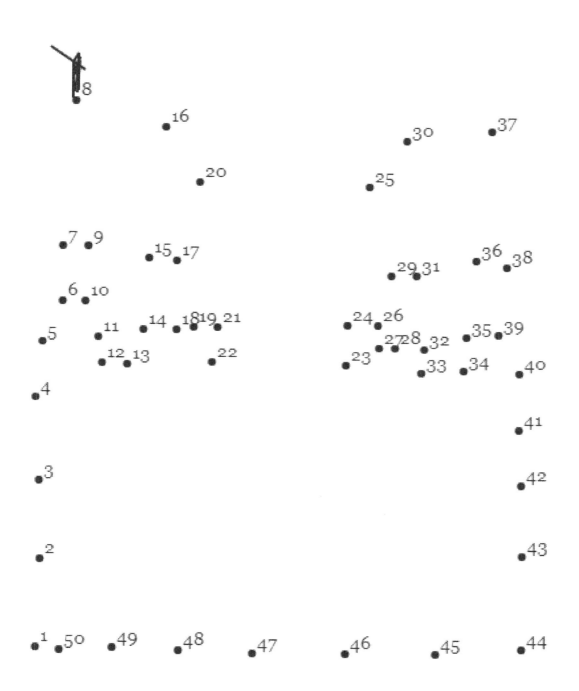

3

What is this building?

T_m_l_

#4

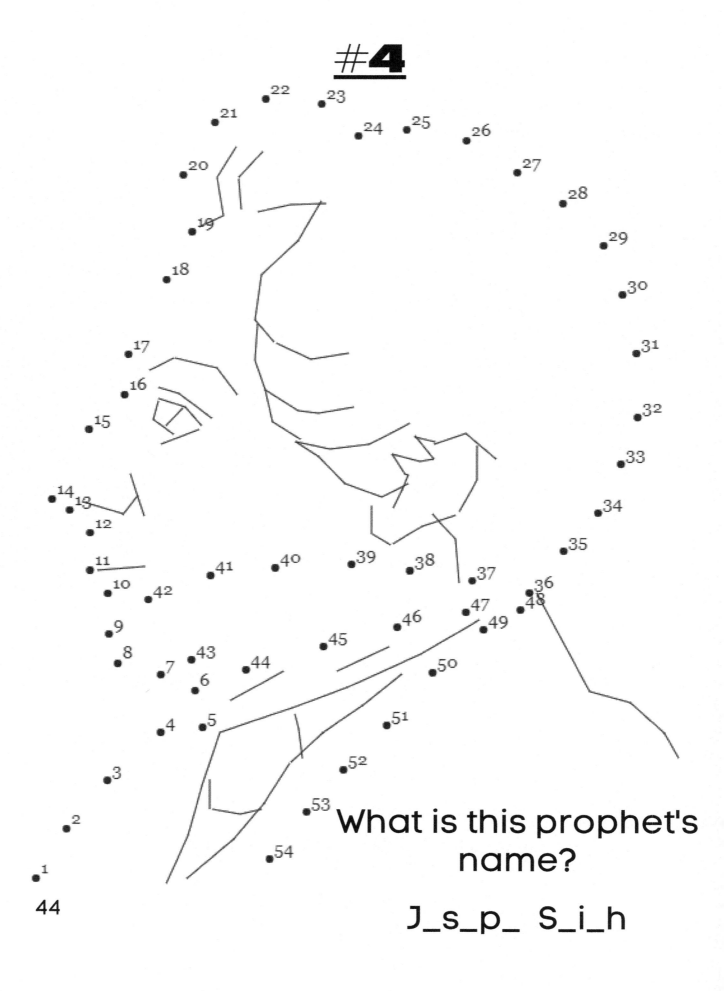

What is this prophet's name?

44

J_s_p_ S_i_h

#5

What child is this?

B_b_ J_s_s

45

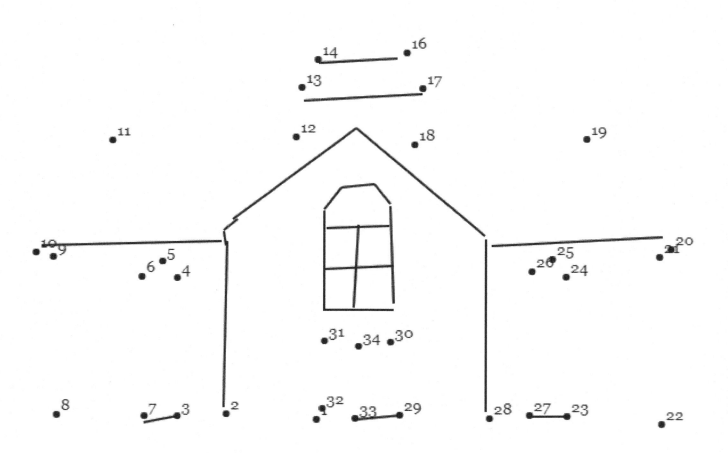

What is this building?

c_a_e_

46

Bingo

CONFERENCE BINGO

Level 1

HOW TO PLAY

Before Conference begins -- Fill in the bingo card with random church-related words/pictures that you often hear at church, in the scriptures or during General Conference.

As you listen to Conference, when you hear a word you wrote down, color that box. Listen carefully and see if you can have all of your boxes colored before the last session of conference is over!

You can even copy this blank page and share with a family member so they can fill in their own words and see who completes their BINGO first!

CONFERENCE BiNGO
Level 2

Faith	Nephi	Trials	Love
Satan	Temples	Hope	Service
Family	Sunday	Prayer	Moses
Patience	Joseph Smith	Tithing	Israel

HOW TO PLAY

This Bingo Card already has church-related words that are often used in Church or General Conference filled in!

As you listen to Conference, when you hear a word on this card, color that box. Listen carefully and see if you can have all of your boxes colored before the last session of conference is over!

CONFERENCE BINGO

Level 2

HOW TO PLAY

Before Conference begins -- Fill in the bingo card with random church-related words that you often hear at church, in the scriptures or during General Conference.

As you listen to Conference, when you hear a word you wrote down, color that box. Listen carefully and see if you can have all of your boxes colored before the last session of conference is over!

You can even copy this blank page and share with a family member so they can fill in their own words and see who completes their BINGO first!

CONFERENCE BINGO
Level 3

HOW TO PLAY

Before Conference begins -- Fill in the bingo card with random church-related words that you often hear at church, in the scriptures or during General Conference.

As you listen to Conference, when you hear a word you wrote down, color that box. Listen carefully and see if you can have all of your boxes colored before the last session of conference is over!

You can even copy this blank page and share with a family member so they can fill in their own words and see who completes their BINGO first!

Who's Talking Now?

WHO'S TALKING NOW?

As you listen to the speakers during General Conference draw their facial features: hair, eyes, nose, mouth, and add any background that you see. You can even add a tie and/or glasses.
If it's a female speaker you can change the clothing to match what she is wearing!

My name is

WHO'S TALKING NOW?

As you listen to the speakers during General Conference draw their facial features: hair, eyes, nose, mouth, and add any background that you see. You can even add a tie and/or glasses.
If it's a female speaker you can change the clothing to match what she is wearing!

My name is

- -

WHO'S TALKING NOW?

As you listen to the speakers during General Conference draw their facial features: hair, eyes, nose, mouth, and add any background that you see. You can even add a tie and/or glasses.
If it's a female speaker you can change the clothing to match what she is wearing!

My name is

WHO'S TALKING NOW?

As you listen to the speakers during General Conference draw their facial features: hair, eyes, nose, mouth, and add any background that you see. You can even add a tie and/or glasses.
If it's a female speaker you can change the clothing to match what she is wearing!

My name is

- -

WHO'S TALKING NOW?

As you listen to the speakers during General Conference draw their facial features: hair, eyes, nose, mouth, and add any background that you see. You can even add a tie and/or glasses.
If it's a female speaker you can change the clothing to match what she is wearing!

My name is

WHO'S TALKING NOW?

As you listen to the speakers during General Conference draw their facial features: hair, eyes, nose, mouth, and add any background that you see. You can even add a tie and/or glasses.
If it's a female speaker you can change the clothing to match what she is wearing!

My name is

WHO'S TALKING NOW?

As you listen to the speakers during General Conference draw their facial features: hair, eyes, nose, mouth, and add any background that you see. You can even add a tie and/or glasses.
If it's a female speaker you can change the clothing to match what she is wearing!

My name is

WHO'S TALKING NOW?

As you listen to the speakers during General Conference draw their facial features: hair, eyes, nose, mouth, and add any background that you see. You can even add a tie and/or glasses.
If it's a female speaker you can change the clothing to match what she is wearing!

My name is

60

WHO'S TALKING NOW?

As you listen to the speakers during General Conference draw their facial features: hair, eyes, nose, mouth, and add any background that you see. You can even add a tie and/or glasses.
If it's a female speaker you can change the clothing to match what she is wearing!

My name is

WHO'S TALKING NOW?

As you listen to the speakers during General Conference draw their facial features: hair, eyes, nose, mouth, and add any background that you see. You can even add a tie and/or glasses.
If it's a female speaker you can change the clothing to match what she is wearing!

My name is

WHO'S TALKING NOW?

As you listen to the speakers during General Conference draw their facial features: hair, eyes, nose, mouth, and add any background that you see. You can even add a tie and/or glasses.
If it's a female speaker you can change the clothing to match what she is wearing!

My name is

WHO'S TALKING NOW?

As you listen to the speakers during General Conference draw their facial features: hair, eyes, nose, mouth, and add any background that you see. You can even add a tie and/or glasses.
If it's a female speaker you can change the clothing to match what she is wearing!

My name is

WHO'S TALKING NOW?

As you listen to the speakers during General Conference draw their facial features: hair, eyes, nose, mouth, and add any background that you see. You can even add a tie and/or glasses.
If it's a female speaker you can change the clothing to match what she is wearing!

My name is

WHO'S TALKING NOW?

As you listen to the speakers during General Conference draw their facial features: hair, eyes, nose, mouth, and add any background that you see. You can even add a tie and/or glasses.
If it's a female speaker you can change the clothing to match what she is wearing!

My name is

WHO'S TALKING NOW?

As you listen to the speakers during General Conference draw their facial features: hair, eyes, nose, mouth, and add any background that you see. You can even add a tie and/or glasses.
If it's a female speaker you can change the clothing to match what she is wearing!

My name is

Mazes

Maze 1-1

It's Sunday morning. Help my family find our way to church.

Maze 2-1

"I love to see the temple. I'm going there some day"
Help me find my way to the temple.

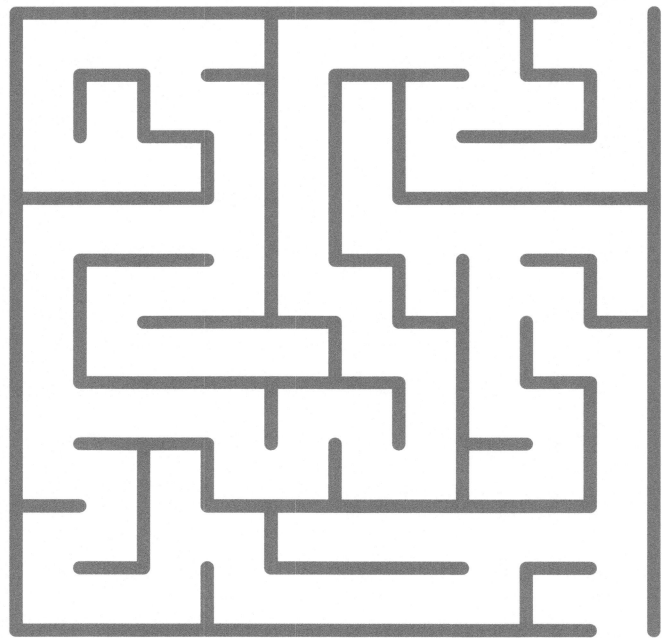

Maze 3-1

Maze 4-1

Maze 5-1

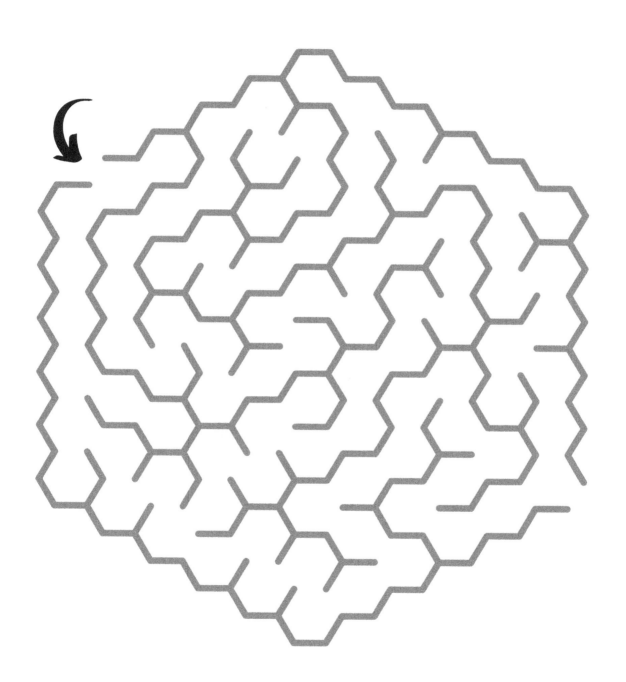

Maze 6-1

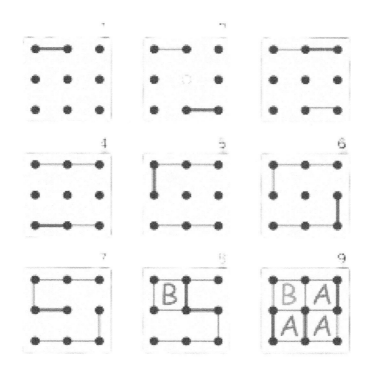

Dots and Boxes

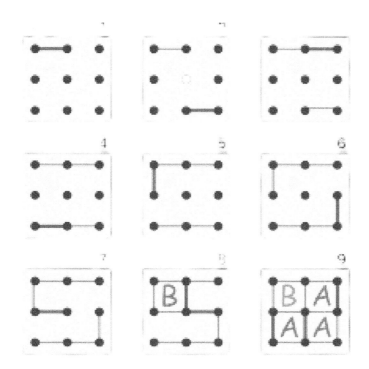

How to play - Two players take turns adding a single horizontal or vertical line between two adjacent dots The player who completes the fourth side of a 1x1 box puts their initial in the box and takes another turn. When all the boxes are completed the player with the most boxes wins.

Tic-Tac-Toe

How to play - Each player picks a symbol to represent them - X's or O's. Alternating turns each player picks one empty space and writes their symbol in it. The first player to get three in a row wins.

Puzzle Solutions

I Spy - Springtime - Answers

5   8   6   9   7   9   7

I Spy - Home - Answers

12   7   11   9   9   7   7

Spot the Difference #1 - Answers

Second picture has:

** 2 flying birds instead of one

**Only 3 flowers

**A shovel in the sandbox

**Only 2 apples in the tree

**No heart on girl's shirt.

Spot the Difference #2 - Answers

Second picture has:

** No rain

**Family in front of church

**Dog is facing the other direction

**6 apples in the big tree

**No face on the sun

I Love to See the Temple - Solution

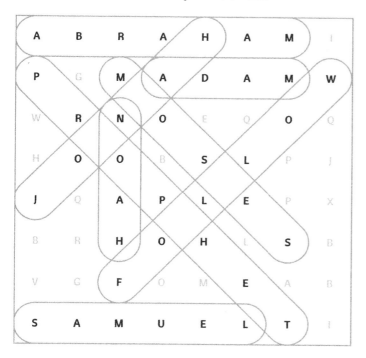

I Am a Child of God - Solution

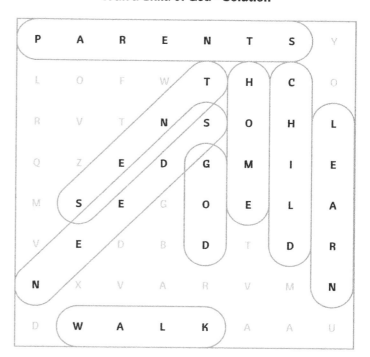

Follow the Prophet - Solution

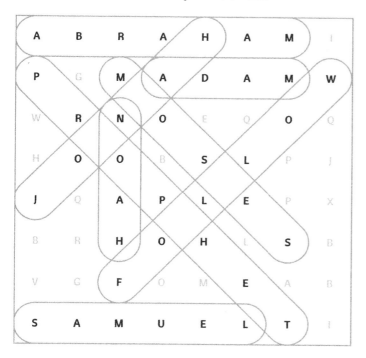

Families Can Be Together Forever - Solution

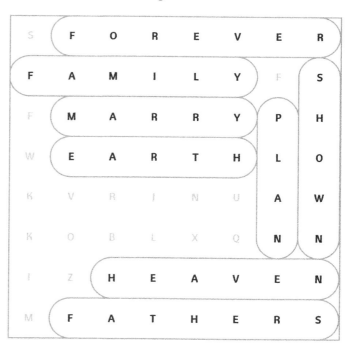

I Know My Father Lives - Solution

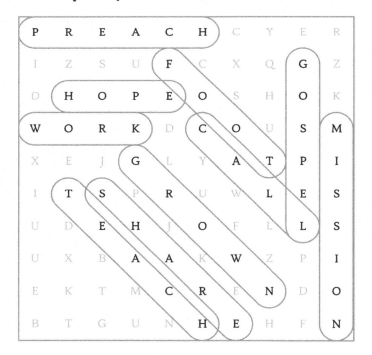

I Lived in Heaven - Solution

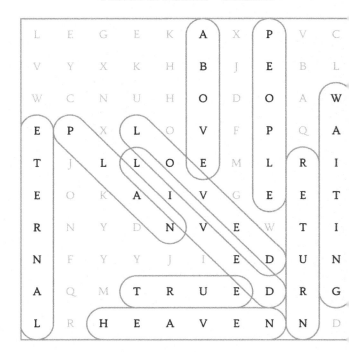

I Hope They Call Me On a Mission - Solution

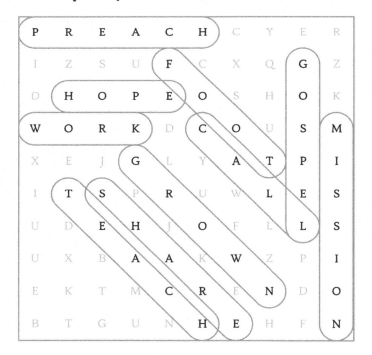

Book of Mormon Stories - Solution

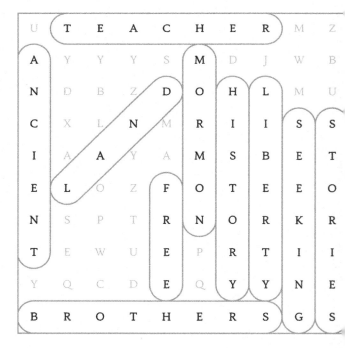

CHALLENGE - Old Testament Prophets - Solution

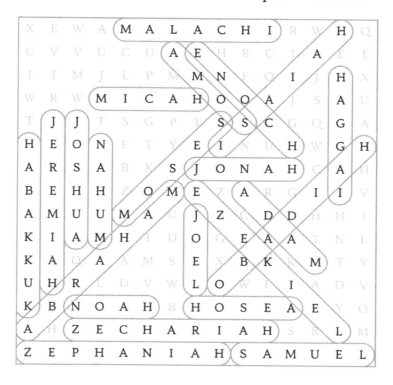

CHALLENGE - First Presidency & 12 Apostles - Solution

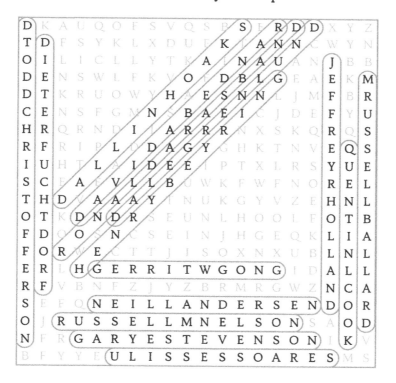

Sudoku 6 x 6 Solutions

Puzzle #1

2	3	4	5	6	1
1	5	6	3	2	4
6	2	5	1	4	3
4	1	3	2	5	6
3	6	2	4	1	5
5	4	1	6	3	2

Puzzle #2

3	6	4	5	1	2
1	2	5	3	6	4
2	1	6	4	5	3
4	5	3	6	2	1
6	3	1	2	4	5
5	4	2	1	3	6

Puzzle #3

1	2	3	4	6	5
4	5	6	3	2	1
3	1	2	5	4	6
6	4	5	2	1	3
5	6	4	1	3	2
2	3	1	6	5	4

Puzzle #4

1	5	3	6	2	4
4	2	6	1	3	5
6	4	1	2	5	3
5	3	2	4	1	6
2	6	5	3	4	1
3	1	4	5	6	2

Sudoku 9 x 9 Solutions

Puzzle #1

8	1	5	9	7	4	2	6	3
9	2	4	5	6	3	1	8	7
7	6	3	8	2	1	9	5	4
3	7	2	4	9	5	8	1	6
6	5	1	2	3	8	7	4	9
4	9	8	6	1	7	5	3	2
5	8	9	3	4	2	6	7	1
1	3	6	7	8	9	4	2	5
2	4	7	1	5	6	3	9	8

Puzzle #2

6	3	9	7	1	4	2	8	5
5	7	2	6	3	8	9	1	4
1	8	4	5	2	9	3	7	6
3	9	5	1	6	7	8	4	2
8	2	1	3	4	5	7	6	9
4	6	7	8	9	2	1	5	3
7	1	6	9	5	3	4	2	8
9	4	8	2	7	6	5	3	1
2	5	3	4	8	1	6	9	7

Puzzle #3

9	1	6	3	2	4	7	5	8
8	3	2	7	6	5	1	9	4
4	7	5	1	9	8	2	6	3
6	8	4	9	1	7	5	3	2
1	5	9	2	8	3	4	7	6
7	2	3	4	5	6	9	8	1
5	6	7	8	4	2	3	1	9
2	9	8	5	3	1	6	4	7
3	4	1	6	7	9	8	2	5

Puzzle #4

1	8	5	3	4	6	2	7	9
6	3	4	9	7	2	1	8	5
9	2	7	1	8	5	6	4	3
5	7	9	8	6	4	3	2	1
2	1	8	5	9	3	4	6	7
3	4	6	2	1	7	9	5	8
8	5	3	4	2	1	7	9	6
7	9	2	6	3	8	5	1	4
4	6	1	7	5	9	8	3	2

2022 12 APOSTLES

M URSESLL ALABDRL	M RUSSELL BALLARD
TEDEIR F CUTOFHDR	DIETER F UCHTDORF
IREGTR W OGGN	GERRIT W GONG
ERFYEFJ R LHNAODL	JEFFREY R HOLLAND
AEDL G LDNRUNE	DALE G RENLUND
IENL L ENANERSD	NEIL L ANDERSEN
TNNQUIE L KCOO	QUENTIN L COOK
SLSISUE EASSRO	ULISSES SOARES
OARLDN A ASNDARB	RONALD A RASBAND
D DOTD OSTRIHCFOEFNRS	D TODD CHRISTOFFERSON
AVDID A DAENBR	DAVID A BEDNAR
YAGR E TESSVNEON	GARY E STEVENSON

BAPTISM RELATED WORDS

CESDRA	SACRED
VNANTECO	COVENANT
BMEEMR	MEMBER
EBIDAPZT	BAPTIZED
ENIMOSIMR	IMMERSION
YLHO HGSTO	HOLY GHOST
SJUSE SHCTRI	JESUS CHRIST
DMNSTONEACMM	COMMANDMENTS
ETIHW TCOSHLE	WHITE CLOTHES
TIOPDSHERO	PRIESTHOOD
ATRWE	WATER
MTOOCIANNFIR	CONFIRMATION

OLD TESTAMENT PROPHETS #1

AKBKHKUA	HABAKKUK
HEPZANIHA	ZEPHANIAH
GGHAAI	HAGGAI
EIAARHZCH	ZECHARIAH
AALMCHI	MALACHI
SAAHII	ISAIAH
DAMA	ADAM
CONEH	ENOCH
RBAAHAM	ABRAHAM
EMOSS	MOSES
HONA	NOAH

OLD TESTAMENT PROPHETS #2

SAUOHJ	JOSHUA
USLEAM	SAMUEL
HIAEJRME	JEREMIAH
ZEKLIEE	EZEKIEL
SHAEO	HOSEA
LEJO	JOEL
MSOA	AMOS
AHOBDAI	OBADIAH
HNAJO	JONAH
ACMIH	MICAH
HNMAU	NAHUM

PLACES IN CHURCH HISTORY

ALPAMRY	PALMYRA
LHLI MUCAORH	HILL CUMORAH
TKRIANDL	KIRTLAND
ANUOOV	NAUVOO
RFA EWTS	FAR WEST
ANCJKOS UYOTCN	JACKSON COUNTY
LSTA KLEA YCIT	SALT LAKE CITY
OAHRYMN	HARMONY
CSDREA OVREG	SACRED GROVE
NETIRW RARUSTEQ	WINTER QUARTERS
AGACTHRE	CARTHAGE
ITRLBEY IJAL	LIBERTY JAIL

ORIGINAL 12 APOSTLES

EERPT	PETER
DENWAR	ANDREW
SAMJE	JAMES
NHOJ	JOHN
HTEDDUSA	THADDEUS
IHIPLP	PHILIP
MTERHOWBA	BARTHOMEW
HMTSAO	THOMAS
ISMON	SIMON
AJDSU ORIATISC	JUDAS ISCARIOT
EAJSM	JAMES
EMTTHAW	MATTHEW

BOOK OF MORMON PROPHETS #1

HINPE	NEPHI
BOCJA	JACOB
ONSE	ENOS
NIBIADA	ABINADI
IGKN EAIBNNMJ	KING BENJAMIN
AOMISH	MOSIAH
MLAA	ALMA
LMAA ETH GRNOEYU	ALMA THE YOUNGER
NRMIOO	MORONI
OMROMN	MORMON

BOOK OF MORMON PROPHETS #2

ERJDA	JARED
OEHTRBR FO AJDRE	BROTHER OF JARED
HETER	ETHER
AHNEMAL	HELAMAN
OMMAN	AMMON
RAAON	AARON
MRIEHN	HIMNER
NATIAPC OIOMRN	CAPTAIN MORONI
IELH	LEHI
IHBAS	ABISH
ULSEAM	SAMUEL

BOOK OF MORMON 12 APOSTLES		7 DISPENSATION LEADERS	
IPEHN	NEPHI		
ITTMHYO	TIMOTHY	DAMA	ADAM
NOASJ	JONAS		
ITMNAHO	MATHONI	HENCO	ENOCH
AAOIMHHNTH	MATHONIHAH		
MUKNE	KUMEN	ONAH	NOAH
MUKHEOINN	KUMENONHI		
IHEEJARM	JEREMIAH	RBAMHAA	ABRAHAM
OMHSNEN	SHEMNON		
OANSJ	JONAS	OSMES	MOSES
EHEAKIDZ	ZEDEKIAH		
HAIIAS	ISAIAH	IHRTCS	CHRIST
		SOEJHP IHTMS	JOSEPH SMITH

Dot-to-Dot Answers

1. Book of Mormon
2. Choose the Right
3. Temple
4. Joseph Smith
5. Baby Jesus
6. Chapel

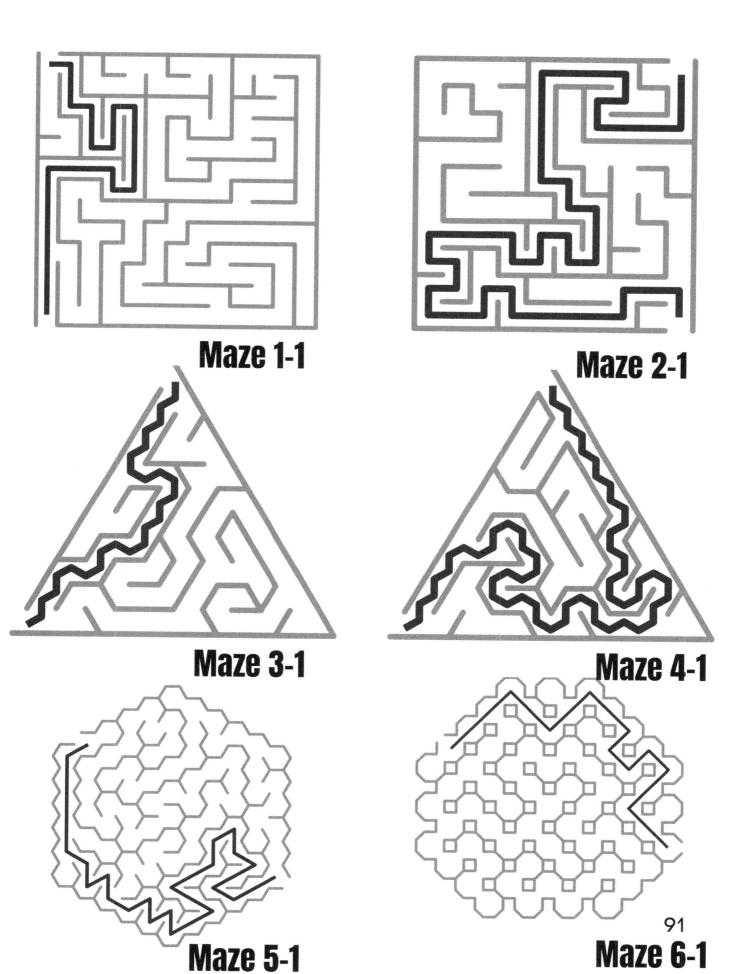

Maze 1-1

Maze 2-1

Maze 3-1

Maze 4-1

Maze 5-1

Maze 6-1

91

Made in the USA
Las Vegas, NV
24 March 2023